cool!

Brain Box

WOW!

Cool Kid

bright spark

out of this world

Great idea!

at English

excellent!

Boo!

WOW!

teacher's pet

so true...

100% FACT

Super Star

Know it all!

!

high flyer

WELL HARD

time for tea !

!

English Whizz

No. 1

?

out of this world

hard cheese

?

Know it all!

Star pupil

FAB!

I DON'T BELIEVE IT!!

Huh

easy peasy

Great idea!

TOP MARKS

10 out of 10

rocket science

FAB!

HELP!

leaps ahead

?

RHYME TIME

Boo!

easy peasy

No. 1

cool!

10 out of 10

TOP MARKS

time for English

out of this world

out of this world

!

full speed ahead

The story so far...

WELL HARD

Huh

rocket science

over the moon

high flyer

?

FAB!

ENGLISH EXPERT

TOP MARKS

time for tea

Top Dog

No. 1

Fab at English

out of this world

easy peasy

100% FACT

?

hard cheese

100% Fiction

1st place

TOP MARKS

!

FAB!

TOP MARKS

Huh

high flyer

a piece of cake

well done!

over the moon

10 out of 10

MEGA

so true...

out of this world

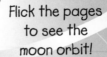

Flick the pages to see the moon orbit!

Mega English age 5-7

Contributions by Nicola Morgan and Lindsay Hancock
Illustrated by John Haslam, Pip Adams and Craig Cameron

Look out for me! I'm here to explain everything to you and help if you get stuck.

Published in Great Britain by Egmont Books Limited,
239 Kensington High Street, London W8 6SA.
Printed in Italy.
ISBN 0 7498 5770 6
3 5 7 9 10 8 6 4 2

Mega English
Contents

100 stickers

3

About this book

Mega English 5–7 offers lots of practice in English skills as described in the guidelines for the National Literacy Strategy. The book reflects the content of the National Curriculum in England and Wales and the 5–14 programme in Scotland.

The book is divided into three sections. The content of each section reflects what is taught from the National Literacy Strategy.

1) Reading Comprehension
2) Spelling Skills
3) Writing Composition

This book is aimed at children aged 5–7 years. It covers work done in school in Reception, Year 1 and Year 2, so don't be concerned if your 5-year-old needs help with many of the activities. This is to be expected. Some topics may seem ambitious but these are aimed at 7-year-olds.

Activities within each section are progressive, but you can choose to do a little at a time from each section if your child prefers this. The main aim is to start with something that interests your child and that he or she will feel confident about tackling.

Answers appear at the end of each section, so that either you or your child can check and mark the work. After each answer section is a list of useful words and a check-list which will help you and your child to record progress made.

Your child can add the 100 fun stickers to the pages of the book, or use them to decorate pencil cases, posters or other items.

Finding your way around

Flick the pages to see the moon orbit!

Check-list to tick off your child's achievements.

Explanation pages with examples to come back to, if your child needs help.

Useful words your child will have learnt in each section.

What your child will learn in each section.

How to help your child

Let your child decide how long he or she wants to work on the book. The book is designed for your child to start and stop any time he or she wishes. Give lots of encouragement and praise for effort.

Instructions are written clearly and simply, but you will need to look through the activities and explain what your child is being asked to do. If your child has problems with a type of activity, talk about it together and try to help. You may need to discuss it with your child's class teacher.

How...

...to understand fiction and non-fiction

In this reading comprehension section, you will be reading pieces of **fiction** and pieces of **non-fiction**.

You will need to answer questions in the same way for both.

Fiction is everything that is made up or pretend, not real.
Fiction includes stories, poems and plays.
There are different types of story, for example:
adventure, ghost, fairy and love stories.

Non-fiction is anything that is real or true, not pretend.
Non-fiction includes newspapers, encyclopedias, textbooks and maps.

This book has real facts in, so it is non-fiction.

All the stories in this book are made up, so it is fiction.

Here are some pages from fiction and non-fiction books.

Read each page carefully and decide whether it is from a fiction or non-fiction book.

Write 'fiction' or 'non-fiction' under each page.

Once upon a time, Mother Bear made some porridge.

One day, Splot the alien kidnapped our teacher and turned him into a beetle.

1. Stir the sugar with the butter.

2. Next add the currants and raisins.

3. Add a pinch of salt and sift in the flour.

150 million years ago, dinosaurs walked the Earth. Some even flew in the air like birds. People have found fossils of many dinosaurs and plants.

How...

...to do reading comprehension

Reading comprehension is a way of checking that you have understood what you have been reading. The following pages have many pieces of writing to read and questions to answer.

Read the piece of writing as many times as you like before you answer the questions.

There are two different ways to answer the questions:
1. Tick the box with the correct answer.
2. Answer the question in a sentence.

When answering the questions, you will be learning different reading comprehension skills:

How to look for facts.
How to understand why things happen.
How to understand what's going on.
How to look for words and understand what they mean.

Parent note:
With a 5-year-old or beginning reader you will need to read the passages and discuss the answers together.

Look at this example that has been filled in for you.

Billy's Big Match

Billy loved to play football. His favourite position was centre-forward. He loved scoring goals and hearing the crowd chant his name. Little was Billy to realise that the next game he would play would change his life forever ...

1. What does Billy love to do?

	play rugby		go to school
	eat chocolate	✓	play football

2. What position does Billy love to play?

	goalie	✓	centre-forward
	right back		midfield

3. What word means to sing or shout?   chant

4. What will happen in the next game?

Billy's life will change forever.

The Christmas Dog

One week after Christmas, Sally and Ben found a little dog on the doorstep. He looked tired and cold and very hungry.

"You poor thing," said Dad. "Let's give you some food and water and get you warm."

"Can't we keep him?" asked Ben.

"No, he belongs to someone else," replied Dad. "His owner will be missing him."

I. When did the children find the dog?

| | on Christmas day | | a week before Christmas |
| | on the doorstep | | a week after Christmas |

2. Who wanted to keep the dog?

| | Sally | | Ben |
| | Dad | | the dog |

3. Why did Dad say they could not keep the dog?

_____

_____

_____

Sally and Ben gave the little dog food and made a cosy bed for him near the fire. They wished they could keep him. But that evening a man from a special dog home took the dog away. Sally and Ben were very sad.

A week later, Mum came home with a big box. In it was the little dog! "We can keep the dog because his owner doesn't want him any more," she said.

"Hooray!" shouted Sally and Ben in delight. "Let's call him 'Christmas'," said Sally.

4. Where did the children make a bed for the dog?

☐	**in a big box**	☐	**in a special dog home**
☐	**near the fire**	☐	**in the kitchen**

5. Why were they able to keep the dog?

☐	**because they wanted him**	☐	**because his owner didn't want him**
☐	**because it was Christmas**	☐	**because they were sad**

6. How did they feel when Mum said they could keep the dog?

_____

7. Did you like the end of this story? Why?

_____

_____

The Big Surprise

Jack found some seeds in the garden shed. He planted one in some soil in a small pot. He put some water on the soil and left the pot in a sunny place. Each day he looked to see if anything was growing. Sometimes he put more water on the soil.

After ten days a small green leaf appeared. "Hooray!" said Jack. "I wonder what it is?"

1. Where did Jack find the seeds?

☐ **in the soil** ☐ **in a sunny place**

☐ **in the garden shed** ☐ **in the water**

2. How often did Jack water the soil?

☐ **every day** ☐ **never**

☐ **sometimes** ☐ **twice**

3. Why did Jack say "Hooray!" when he saw the leaf?

_____

_____

_____

In the next week, the plant grew, and grew. Mum said it needed a bigger pot so she helped Jack to move it.

Soon the plant had ten leaves and was too big for its new pot. It was almost as tall as Jack.

"I still don't know what sort of plant it is," said Jack. "Do you know, Mum?"

Mum didn't say anything, she just smiled.

4. What did Mum and Jack do to the plant?

| | they made it bigger | | they put it in a bigger pot |

| | they put it in the garden | | they tied it to a stick |

5. Why did the plant need a bigger pot again?

_____

_____

6. How tall was the plant?

| | taller than Jack | | as tall as Mum |

| | nearly as tall as Jack | | ten metres tall |

7. On this page, did Mum tell Jack what the plant was?

_____

The plant grew taller and taller. Mum planted it in the garden and Jack could see it from his bedroom window.

One night, Mum read Jack a bedtime story called *Jack and the Beanstalk*. In the story, the beanstalk grew as high as the clouds and there was an angry giant living at the top with lots of gold.

"Maybe my plant is a beanstalk!" shouted Jack. "Maybe I will find gold at the top of it!"

"Well, don't try climbing it," said Mum firmly. "You might fall."

8. What was Jack's bedtime story called?

_____

_____

9. In the story, who lived at the top of the beanstalk?

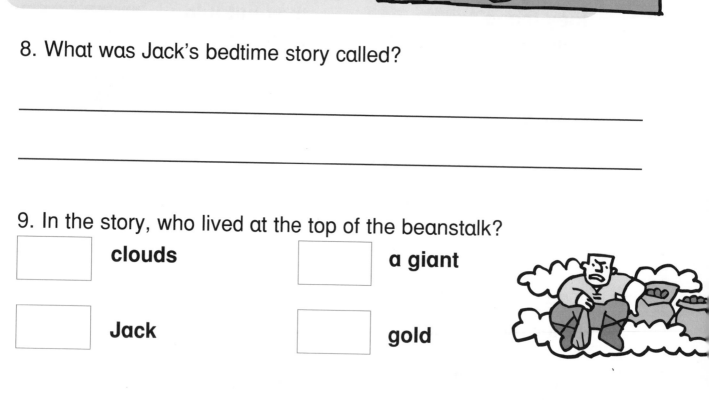

| | clouds | | a giant |
| | Jack | | gold |

10. Why didn't Mum want Jack to climb the plant?

| | because it was bedtime | | because she didn't like gold |
| | because he might fall | | because of the angry giant |

The next day Jack went outside to play. When he saw his plant, his eyes opened wide in surprise.

"Mum, Mum, Mum. Come and look!" he yelled. Mum came running, thinking that something terrible had happened. She saw the plant. It had a huge yellow flower at the top, with a round brown middle.

"It's a sunflower!" she said. "And it's taller than me. We must enter it for the flower show – it might win a prize."

Jack looked after his plant very well. And, guess what? He did win first prize at the show, which was much better than an angry giant and lots of gold.

11. What colour was the middle of the flower?

☐ **yellow**   ☐ **green**

☐ **brown**

12. Why did Mum think something terrible had happened?

_____

_____

13. Where did Jack win a prize for his sunflower?

☐ **because it was tall**   ☐ **in the garden**

☐ **at the flower show**   ☐ **in a pot**

Water, Lovely Water

Many hundreds of miles away in Africa, a girl called Kuma lived with her family. Everyone in Kuma's village helped to work on the land. They grew fruit and vegetables and kept animals too.

They grew their own food, but if there was any spare food they would sell it at the market. With the money this made they could buy the things which they couldn't grow, like clothes, soap, oil and tools. They kept cows and goats, which they could sell as well. The cows and goats gave them milk.

Everyone had to work hard. But the worst thing was that they had no water in the village. Every day, all the women had to carry heavy jars of water from the river. The water was dirty and sometimes made people ill. The women did not complain. They had been doing it for years, and they needed the water for themselves, their animals and to grow their food.

I. How far away is Africa?

☐ nearby

☐ hundreds of miles away

☐ thousands of miles away

☐ far away

2. Where did the people go to sell things?

| | the village | | the market |

| | a farm | | a shop |

3. Write three things the story says people needed but couldn't grow.

| | | |

4. Who had to work hard?

| | Kuma | | animals |

| | everyone | | they didn't work hard |

5. What was the biggest problem the villagers had?

6. Who fetched water every day?

| | Kuma | | everyone |

| | the children | | all the women |

7. There were two reasons why the women did not complain. Tick the two that you learn from the story.

| | they had been doing it for years | | they had nothing else to do |

| | water helped their food to grow |

17

Then one day, some strangers arrived in the village with a lot of trucks and diggers. They talked to the leaders of the village and the leaders started to look very pleased. But they wouldn't say why. They said it was a secret, and that Kuma and her friends must wait and see.

Kuma could see that something was happening. Then the huge digging machines thundered about. Men with hard hats on shouted and pipes were put into the ground. Kuma and her friends watched and wondered. Then at last it was finished. Everyone came to see.

The women from the village performed a special dance and the chief made a long speech which Kuma thought was boring. "Hurry up and get on with it!" she whispered to herself.

The chief pulled a big metal handle up and down. And suddenly, Kuma's eyes were wide with amazement. Clear, gushing water, right in the middle of the village. Everybody cheered. Kuma tasted the water – it was delicious!

Life in the village was much better after that. Especially for the women, who never had to carry heavy jars of dirty water again.

8. Two types of **machine** are mentioned on page 18. What are they?

9. What word tells you that the diggers were noisy?

10. Did the men talk quietly? ☐ **yes** ☐ **no**

11. Why do you think that is?

_____

_____

12. What did Kuma think of the chief's speech?

☐ **special** ☐ **boring** ☐ **exciting**

13. How did the chief make water come out?

☐ **he turned the big tap** ☐ **he pulled the handle up and down**

☐ **it just gushed out by itself** ☐ **he got water from the well**

14. Why was life so much better for the women?

_____

_____

How...

...to understand poetry

Poetry is very special in the way it uses words.
It uses words that **rhyme** and sentences that have **rhythm**.

A rhyme is when two words sound the same.
The rhyming words are underlined here.

> **One, two, three, four, <u>five</u>,**
> **Once I caught a fish <u>alive</u>.**
> **Six, seven, eight, nine, <u>ten</u>,**
> **Then I let it go <u>again</u>.**

Other words that rhyme are: **dive, hive; pen, men.**

The rhythm of the poem is the beat of the words in the sentence.
Clap your hands on each beat of the word as you read this poem
out loud.

> **Lon-don Bridge is fall-ing down,**
> **Fall-ing down, fall-ing down.**
> **Lon-don Bridge is fall-ing down,**
> **My fair la-dy.**

The Owl and the Pussy-Cat

The Owl and the Pussy-Cat went to sea
In a beautiful pea-green boat,
They took some honey, and plenty of money,
Wrapped up in a five-pound note.
The Owl looked up to the stars above,
And sang to a small guitar,
"O lovely Pussy! O Pussy, my love,
"What a beautiful Pussy you are,
"You are,
"You are!
"What a beautiful Pussy you are!"

1. Who went to sea?

_____

_____

2. Name two things about the boat.

_____

_____

3. What did they take to eat?

☐ **honey**   ☐ **money**

☐ **peas**

4. Did you like this poem? Why?

_____

_____

How...

...to understand non-fiction

The next few exercises are all **non-fiction**.
Remember: non-fiction is true and real, not made up.
Some of the exercises look different, but answer the questions in the same way.

Here are some things to remember when doing the following exercises:

An invitation is like a set of instructions.
It tells you what you are being invited to, the time and place and whether you should bring anything.

A recipe has a list and some instructions.
The **list** tells you everything you will need (the ingredients).
The **instructions** tell you what to do.

An encyclopedia is an information book.
Everything is in a special order so you can easily look up what you want to know.
Encyclopedias give you lots and lots of information.

I. Imagine that you **can** go to the party. Fill in the reply card.

2. How old will Sam be?

3. What sort of birthday party will it be?

4. What time will the party start?

☐ **4 o'clock**	☐ **Saturday 8th November**
☐ **2.30**	☐ **2 o'clock**

5. Name two things the guests must bring to the party.

23

Chocolate Biscuit Cake

Ingredients:
I packet digestive biscuits
75g butter
4 tablespoons cocoa powder
3 tablespoons syrup

I Crush the biscuits into crumbs.

2 Melt the butter in a large saucepan over a gentle heat.

3 Turn the heat off and mix the cocoa powder and syrup into the butter.

4 Pour the biscuit crumbs into the saucepan and mix well.

5 Tip the mixture into a greased, shallow tin and press down firmly all over. Put it in the fridge until it is hard.
Cut into pieces.

I. What do you do with the biscuits?

☐ **melt them over a gentle heat** ☐ **crush them into crumbs**

☐ **mix the cocoa powder in** ☐ **cut them into pieces**

2. How much cocoa powder do you need?

☐ **75g** ☐ **4 tablespoons** ☐ **I packet**

3. Why does it tell you to use a large saucepan?

_____

_____

4. Which of these things is **not** needed in this recipe?

☐ **cocoa** ☐ **butter** ☐ **eggs**

Africa

Africa is the second largest continent after Asia. It contains over 50 countries. In the north there is a huge desert called the Sahara Desert. Further south are forests and grasslands where animals such as giraffes and elephants live. The River Nile is the longest river in the world. It is 6,741 kilometres (4,187 miles) long.

1. What is the largest continent?

2. Where, in Africa, is the Sahara Desert?

| | north | | south |

| | east | | west |

3. Name two animals that live in the south of Africa?

| | koala bears | | giraffes |

| | elephants | | squirrels |

4. How many miles long is the River Nile?

Deserts

A desert is a very dry land where there is hardly any rain. In the day, it can be so hot that you could fry an egg on the ground. But during the night it is sometimes so cold that water would freeze. This is because there are no clouds to keep the earth warm when the sun is not there.

Many deserts are covered in sand. But some have mountains, rocks, pebbles, or lakes that have dried up in the heat. The Great American Desert has cliffs that the wind has made into amazing and beautiful shapes. The Sahara Desert in Africa is mostly sand. The Australian Desert has red sand.

I. Why is a desert so dry?

| | because it is sandy | | because there is so little rain |
| | because the water is frozen | | because there are no clouds |

2. Is it always hot in a desert?

| | yes | | no |

3. Which desert has beautiful rock shapes?

| | Australian | | Great American |
| | Sahara |

Sometimes it does not rain for a whole year in the desert. But there is water deep under the ground and some plants have roots that go very deep to find it. Other plants have roots that spread out a long way so they can suck up the rain as soon as it falls.

One desert plant is the cactus, which has long, spreading roots. The cactus stores water inside its hard skin. This skin protects it from heat and cold.

Camels are a bit like cactus plants! They store water too – inside their humps. They have special fur which protects them from the sun during the day and keeps them warm at night.

4. Why do some desert plants need deep roots?

5. Find two reasons why a camel is like a cactus:

	it has fur		its skin protects it from the sun and the cold
	it doesn't need water		it stores its water inside itself

6. What is a camel's hump for?

Some other animals live in deserts, too. They have to be very good at seeing and hearing because most of them only come out at night. This is why many desert animals have extra-big eyes or ears.

A desert fox has bigger ears than a normal fox. A gerbil has huge eyes, so that it can see at night. It stays cool in the day by staying underground, like most desert animals.

Some animals don't drink at all. They get water from eating plants. The desert is very difficult to live in and only a few animals can survive there.

7. Why do desert animals have big eyes and ears?

| | **because they live in a desert** | | **because they need to see and hear well at night** |
| | **because the desert is difficult to live in** | | **because they store water in them** |

8. Why do most desert animals stay underground by day?

9. How do some animals manage without drinking at all?

Some people live in the desert but they always make their homes near an oasis. An oasis is where water comes from an underground stream.

Near an oasis, people can grow lots of plants and keep animals such as sheep and goats. They grow apricots, figs, olives, tea and rice.

Life is hard in the desert, for people, animals and plants. But desert people might think that our lives are hard, with our crowded streets and alarm clocks to wake us early every day!

10. What is an oasis?

11. Name four plants which desert people can grow.

12. Why do people live near an oasis?

[ ] because life is hard in a desert   [ ] because they need water for living

[ ] to protect themselves from the sun

13. Would you like to live in the desert? Give one reason for your answer.

Answers

fiction
fiction
non-fiction
non-fiction

The Christmas Dog

1. a week after Christmas
2. Ben
3. he belongs/ed to someone else/
his owner would be missing him,
NOT because they weren't allowed
to/didn't have room

4. near the fire
5. because his owner didn't
want him
6. pleased/delighted, etc
7. any relevant reason

The Big Surprise

1. in the garden shed
2. sometimes
3. anything showing that Jack was
pleased, NOT because he
wondered what it was

4. they put it in a bigger pot
5. because it was too big/had
grown more/was almost as tall
as Jack
6. nearly as tall
as Jack
7. no

8. Jack and the Beanstalk
9. a giant
10. because he might fall

11. brown
12. because Jack shouted/yelled
13. at the flower show

page 16

Water, Lovely Water

1. hundreds of miles away

page 17

2. the market
3. clothes/oil/soap/tools
4. everyone
5. they had no water in the village/ nearby
6. all the women
7. they had been doing it for years AND water helped their food grow

page 19

8. trucks and diggers
9. thundered
10. no
11. so they could be heard/hear each other over the sound of the machines
12. boring
13. he pulled the handle up and down
14. they wouldn't have to carry heavy jars/anything about the women not having to do this work again

page 21

1. the Owl and the Pussy-Cat
2. it was beautiful AND it was pea-green
3. honey

4. any reasonable answer

page 23

1. correct box should be ticked/crossed and name should be written in the space
2. 7/seven
3. swimming
4. 2 o' clock
5. swimming costume/trunks/towel/anything needed for swimming

page 24

1. crush them into crumbs
2. 4 tablespoons
3. so there's enough room for the biscuits/so that it's big enough (NOT to melt the butter)
4. eggs

page 25

1. Asia
2. north
3. giraffes and elephants
4. 4,187 miles NOT 6,741 kilometres

page 26

Deserts

1. because there is so little rain
2. no
3. Great American

page 27

4. because there is water underground/to suck water from deep underground
5. its skin protects it from the sun and the cold AND it stores water inside itself
6. storing water

page 28

7. because they need to see and hear well at night
8. to stay cool/to keep out of the heat/sun
9. they get water from eating plants/by eating plants with water in

page 29

10. a place where water comes from underground/where there is water in the desert
11. apricots/figs/olives/tea/rice
12. because they need water for living
13. any reasonable answer which shows understanding of the passage

How did you do?

Words...

...you have learnt

comprehension
sentence
capital letter
full stop

fiction
pretend
made up
story
adventure story
ghost story
fairy story
love story
poem
poet
rhyme
rhythm

non-fiction
real
true
encyclopedia
newspaper
textbook
map
list
instruction
fact
invitation

After working through each section, put a tick in the box to show how you feel about the topic.

If you tick 'Not sure' go back to those pages and try again.

	Confident	Not sure
The Christmas Dog		
The Big Surprise		
Water, Lovely Water		
The Owl and the Pussy-Cat		
Invitation		
Recipe		
Encyclopedia		
Deserts		

Now you know!

How... ...to spell in different ways

Learning to spell can be tricky, but if you remember a few basic rules and learn these slowly you will get there!

Words fall into two groups when it comes to spelling.

1. Pattern words
- c<u>ar</u>, f<u>ar</u>, st<u>ar</u>t
- f<u>ight</u>, t<u>ight</u>, fr<u>ight</u>ened

These words have the same spelling patterns.

2. Sight words
- said, their, one, many, does

These words don't share a spelling pattern.
You have to learn these by sight.

Pattern words are easy to spell because once you learn the pattern you can spell a whole group of words.

Here are some words with spelling patterns – the patterns have been underlined in each word.

m<u>ug</u>, d<u>ug</u>, l<u>ug</u> and j<u>ug</u> all have the pattern **ug**.

t<u>oa</u>st, g<u>oa</u>t, thr<u>oa</u>t and b<u>oa</u>t all have the pattern **oa**.

th<u>ink</u>, s<u>ink</u>, dr<u>ink</u> and w<u>ink</u> all have the pattern **ink**.

Circle the bit that's the same in each of these words.

car   **far**   **start**   **dart**

Look at these words and circle the bit that's the same in each.

boat   **float**   **coat**   **oat**   **moat**

Now cover them up and spell these.

— — — —   — — — —

Take a look at these words and circle the bit that's the same in each.

fight   **sight**   **right**   **tight**   **light**

How do you spell the word that means
the opposite of day? _____

How...

...to spell with word beginnings

Lots of words have a spelling pattern at the **beginning** of the word.

Sometimes this might be two consonants together:

dr   **gr**   **cr**   **fr**   **br**   **tr**

These letters are called a **consonant cluster**.
The consonants often appear together to make lots of useful words.

Remember:
Vowels are **a, e, i, o, u.**
All the other letters of the alphabet are called consonants!

Spell each word by looking at the picture and slotting in
the letters. Write the word again underneath for practice.

fr

_ _ y   _ _ o s t   _ _ o g

_ _ _   _ _ _ _   _ _ _ _

br

_ _ i d g e   _ _ i c k   _ _ i m

_ _ _ _ _ _   _ _ _ _   _ _ _ _

tr

_ _ e e   _ _ i c k   _ _ a i n

_ _ _ _   _ _ _ _ _   _ _ _ _ _

Here are some more consonant clusters.

dr

_ _ e s s   _ _ a w   _ _ i p

_ _ _ _ _   _ _ _ _   _ _ _ _

gr

_ _ a p e   _ _ o w   _ _ a s s

_ _ _ _ _   _ _ _ _   _ _ _ _ _

cr

_ _ a b   _ _ e a m   _ _ y

_ _ _ _   _ _ _ _ _   _ _ _

cl

_ _ o w n

_ _ _ _ _

_ _ a w

_ _ _ _

_ _ o u d

_ _ _ _ _

pl

_ _ a n e t

_ _ _ _ _ _

_ _ u m

_ _ _ _

_ _ a n t

_ _ _ _ _

fl

_ _ a g

_ _ _ _

_ _ a m e

_ _ _ _ _

_ _ o w e r

_ _ _ _ _ _

HOW...

...to spell with word endings

Lots of words have a spelling pattern at the **end** of a word.

Just like you have seen at the beginning of words, these are consonant clusters too.

ck

ng

nd

lp

st

nk

Do the letter sums to spell the **ck** words.
Draw lines to match the words to the pictures.

du + ck = _ _ _ _

so + ck = _ _ _ _

ki + ck = _ _ _ _

sa + ck = _ _ _ _

ne + ck = _ _ _ _

The letters **ng** come at the end of words.
Write the words that finish the sentences.
Choose from the list.

thing   **king**   **bang**   **ring**   **sing**   **rang**

The _ _ _ _ ruled all the land.

Sarah got a _ _ _ _ for her birthday.

Ben is in the choir. He likes to _ _ _ _ .

The phone _ _ _ _ so I answered it.

Do the letter sums to spell the **nd** words.

a + nd = _ _ _

ha + nd = _ _ _ _

be + nd = _ _ _ _

ba + nd = _ _ _ _

se + nd = _ _ _ _

sta + nd = _ _ _ _ _

The letters **lp** come at the end of words.

Write the words that finish the sentences.
Choose from the list.

pulp   **gulp**   **scalp**   **help**   **yelp**

Jimmy took a big _ _ _ _ of his orange juice.

Karen decided to _ _ _ _ her mum with the shopping.

The puppy let out a _ _ _ _ when the postman walked up the path.

Do the letter sums to spell the **st** words.

be   +   st   =   _ _ _ _

fa   +   st   =   _ _ _ _

la   +   st   =   _ _ _ _

bla   +   st   =   _ _ _ _ _

che   +   st   =   _ _ _ _ _

fore   +   st   =   _ _ _ _ _ _

The letters **nk** come at the end of words.

Write the words that finish the sentences.
Choose from the list.

sink   bank   blink   shrunk   think

Hannah put her pocket money in the _ _ _ _ .

When Joe took his T-shirt out of the washing-machine it
had _ _ _ _ _ _ .

Harold began to _ _ _ _ _ about his summer holiday.

A **singular** word tells you about **one** thing.

A **plural** word tells you about **more than one thing**.

There are different ways to turn a singular into a plural.
The most common way is to add an **s** on the end of the word.

apple	apple**s**	bike	bike**s**

Some plurals are spelt by adding **es** to the end of the word.
These words usually end in **ss**, **ch**, **x** or **sh**.

dress	dress**es**	watch	watch**es**
fox	fox**es**	dish	dish**es**

Words that end with a **y** make plurals in two different ways,
either by adding **s** or **ies**.

day	day**s**	pony	pon**ies**
ray	ray**s**	story	stor**ies**

Some words change altogether, and some don't change at all!

child	**children**	sheep	**sheep**

Look at the singular words.
Spell the plural word underneath each one.

Plurals with s

day   hand   cup   insect

_ _ _ _   _ _ _ _   _ _ _   _ _ _ _ _

cooker   doll   panda

_ _ _ _ _ _   _ _ _ _ _   _ _ _ _ _

Plurals with es

witch   kiss   fox   box

_ _ _ _ _   _ _ _ _ _   _ _ _ _   _ _ _ _

bush   wish   match

_ _ _ _ _ _   _ _ _ _ _   _ _ _ _ _ _

There are two ways of spelling the plurals for words ending in **y**.

vowel + y = s   consonant + y = ies

boy   boys   baby   babies

Spell the plural for these words.

s	
bay	_ _ _ _
tray	_ _ _ _ _
toy	_ _ _ _
key	_ _ _ _

ies	
pony	_ _ _ _ _ _
nappy	_ _ _ _ _ _ _
puppy	_ _ _ _ _ _ _
fairy	_ _ _ _ _ _ _

Now take a look at these words ending in **y**.
Look closely at the letter **before** the **y** and decide
whether the plural is **s** or **ies**.

Singular   **Plural**

party   _____

poppy   _____

play   _____

day   _____

The plural spellings for some words do not follow any rules. Each box has a choice of plural spellings for each word. Circle the correct spelling and then write it underneath.

sheep

sheeps

sheepies

sheep

_ _ _ _ _

tooth

teeth

tooths

toothes

_ _ _ _ _

woman

womanes

women

womans

_ _ _ _ _

child

childies

childes

children

_ _ _ _ _ _ _

man

men

mans

manies

_ _ _

Spelling is a way of using letters to show sounds. Unfortunately, in English, not every sound is spelt the same way.

Look at this example.

Read these words out loud and listen to their sounds.

br**ough**t
alth**ough**
t**ough**
pl**ough**
thr**ough**

These words have the same -ough spelling pattern, but the letters make a completely different sound in each word.

Now look at this example.

Read these words out loud and listen to their sounds.

boat
slow
hole

These words all have a different spelling pattern but they make the same sound!

Here is a sound to listen for.

Write these words with **ee**.

Too many sw _ _ _ _ are bad for your teeth.

The king and qu _ _ _ spent a w _ _ _ at their castle.

Your f _ _ _ smell really bad!

Write these words with **ea**.

I let an old lady sit on my s _ _ _ on the bus.

I made sure my bedroom was n _ _ _ and tidy.

Mum took us to the fair for a tr _ _ _ .

So, **ee** and **ea** can have the same sound!

Look at these pictures and spell each word correctly.

_ _ _ _ _   _ _ _ _ _   _ _ _ _   _ _ _ _

Here is another sound.
Write these words with **oa**.

I can't speak I have a sore t _ _ _ _ _ .

Does ice sink or f _ _ _ _ ?

This sound can also be spelt with **ow**.
Write these words with **ow**.

The infants performed a s _ _ _ for the juniors.

I put my tooth under my p _ _ _ _ _ for the tooth fairy.

Another spelling for this sound is **o_e**.
Write these words with **o_e**.

My dad hit the golf ball into the h _ _ _ .

After going on holiday it's always nice to go back h _ _ _ .

Look at these pictures and spell each word correctly.

_ _ _ _   _ _ _ _   _ _ _ _ _ _

Here is a different sound to listen for.
Write these words with **ie**.

I told a l _ _ to my teacher. She was very cross.

For tea we ate steak and kidney p _ _ .

Now write these words with **igh**.

The opposite of day is n _ _ _ _ .

The box was too h _ _ _ up for me to reach.

Write these words with **y**.

The birds decided to f _ _ south for the winter.

W _ _ did the chicken cross the road?

Look at these pictures and spell each word correctly.

_ _ _ _ _   _ _ _   _ _ _

How...

...to spell other patterns

Some spelling patterns always appear in the same place in a word.

Example:

boy	soil	**oy** and **oi** sound the same.
toy	boil	
bay	train	**ay** and **ai** sound the same.
say	snail	

Rules:

Never use **oi** at the end of a word.
It always goes in the middle of English words.

Never use **ai** at the end of a word.
It always goes in the middle of English words.

If you hear an **oy** sound at the **end** of a word, write **oy**.
If you hear an **ay** sound at the **end** of a word, write **ay**.

Look at these words.

> point   boil   spoil   toy
> enjoy   destroy   annoy

Write the correct words in the spaces.

1. You will _____ me if you _____ my _____ .

2. Don't _____ the soup or you will _____ it.

3. I don't _____ it when you _____ at me.

See if you can complete these words with **oi** or **oy**.

n _ _ s e

b _ _

j _ _

j _ _ n t

t o m b _ _

t o r t _ _ s e

BANG!

POP!

55

Complete these words with **ai** or **ay**.

p _ _ n t

t r _ _ n

p l _ _

s n _ _ l

t r _ _

Some more words to complete with **ai** or **ay**.

f _ _ n t

s w _ _

c l _ _

w _ _ s t

s t _ _

How many words can you make using these letter combinations?

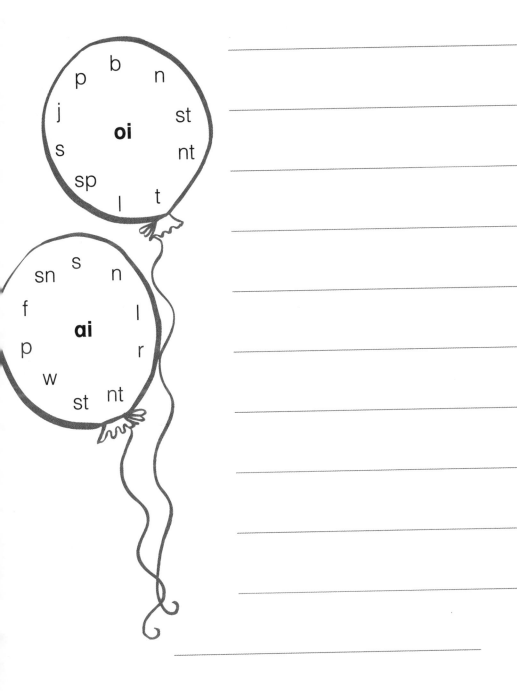

oi

p b n
j   st
s   nt
sp
l   t

ai

sn s n
f   l
p   r
w
st nt

oy

b s
t
ann   ing
tann   pl

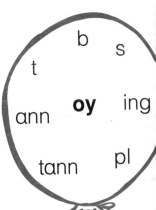

ay

p l n
h   fr
s   d
st   sw
w

Adding **ing** or **ed** to a word makes a brand new word. Here are some of the rules you will need to learn.

There are three ways to add **ing** to a word.

1. Just add **ing**.
sing + ing = singing

2. If the word ends in **e**, lose the **e** before adding **ing**.
give + ing = giving

3. Double the last letter.
hop + ing = hopping

There are three ways to add **ed** to a word.

1. Just add **ed**.
walk + ed = walked

2. If the word ends in **e**, lose the extra **e** before adding **ed**.
dance + ed = danced

3. Double the last letter.
shop + ed = shopped

Here is a long list of words!

Add **ing** to them and remember to double the last letter.

win   <u>w</u> <u>i</u> <u>n</u> <u>n</u> <u>i</u> n g

clap   _ _ _ _ _ _ _ _

sip   _ _ _ _ _ _ _

hop   _ _ _ _ _ _ _

get   _ _ _ _ _ _ _

swim   _ _ _ _ _ _ _ _

cut   _ _ _ _ _ _ _

shop   _ _ _ _ _ _ _ _

run   _ _ _ _ _ _

Spell these words by adding **ing**.
Watch out if the word ends in **e**!

read   r e a d i n g

look   _ _ _ _ _ _ _

smile   _ _ _ _ _ _ _

eat   _ _ _ _ _ _

wave   _ _ _ _ _ _

take   _ _ _ _ _

come   _ _ _ _ _

bite   _ _ _ _ _

sleep   _ _ _ _ _ _ _

Spell these words by adding **ed**.
Watch out if the word ends in **e**!
You may need to double the
last letter.

look   l o o k e d

watch   _ _ _ _ _ _ _

jump   _ _ _ _ _ _

laugh   _ _ _ _ _ _ _

climb   _ _ _ _ _ _ _

clap   _ _ _ _ _ _

share   _ _ _ _ _

hop   _ _ _ _ _

dare   _ _ _ _

Finish the stories below with **ing** and **ed** words.
The words to use have been given to help you.

(walk)

Yesterday I w __ __ __ __ __ up a big hill with my dad.

(climb)

We c __ __ __ __ __ __ up a very steep rock. I could see

(swim)

children s __ __ __ __ __ __ __ in the lake below. Some

(sit)

people were s __ __ __ __ __ __ at the side of the lake.

(shop)

Last Saturday, I went s __ __ __ __ __ __ __ with my

(walk)

mum. On the way to the bus stop we w __ __ __ __ __

(cut)

past a hairdresser's. A lady was c __ __ __ __ __ __

(laugh)

a little girl's hair. We couldn't stop l __ __ __ __ __ __ __

(pull)

because the girl was p __ __ __ __ __ __ a really

grumpy face!

61

...to spell ph and wh words

When **p** and **h** go together they make the sound **f**.
Read these words and listen to the sound **ph** makes.

phone
photo
phrase
tro**ph**y
gra**ph**
geogra**ph**y

The letters **wh** sound like 'w'. The letter **h** is 'silent', which means you only make the 'w' sound.
A lot of **wh** words are question words:

what?
why?
where?
when?
who?

You need to learn which words are spelt with **ph** and which with f. You also need to learn when a 'w' word has a silent 'h'.

There are no rules – you just have to learn them!

Read the words below.

Philip took a photo of a dolphin saying the whole alphabet to an elephant!

ABCDEF GHIJKLM NOPQRS TUVWXYZ

Christopher won a trophy when he took a photo of a pheasant on the phone!

Can you spell all the **ph** words you can see on this page?
The first two are done for you.

Philip   photo   _____

_____   _____   _____

_____   _____   _____

Write **ph** to spell the words.
Spell the words twice more.
Match the words to the pictures.

__ o t o _____ _____

g r a __ _____ _____

__ o n e _____ _____

Spell the correct **ph** words in the spaces.
Choose from the words below.

> alphabet
>
> photos
>
> pheasant
>
> phone

I took lots of _ _ _ _ _ _ on holiday.

My mum keeps on telling me to get off the _ _ _ _ _!

My grandma doesn't eat turkey on Christmas day,
she eats _ _ _ _ _ _ _ _ instead.

I can say the _ _ _ _ _ _ _ _ backwards!

Write **wh** to spell the words.
Draw circles around the words that ask questions.
The first one has been done for you.

__ __ e e l   ⬭w h y⬭   __ __ a t   __ __ i t e

__ __ e n   __ __ e r e   __ __ i c h   __ __ i s p e r

Write **wh** to spell the words.
Choose and spell each one to finish the questions.

__ __ o   __ __ a t   __ __ e r e   __ __ e n   __ __ y   __ __ i c h

__ __ __ __ __ of these buns do you want?

__ __ __ __ is the answer?

__ __ __ __ __ are you going to?

__ __ __ is hiding?

__ __ __ do balls bounce?

__ __ __ __ is your birthday?

65

How...

...to learn sight words

Some words are odd to learn because they don't have a spelling pattern.

These words have to be learned by sight because they have difficult spellings.

Here is a useful method to help you learn tricky sight words.

Look   Say   Cover   Write   Check

Follow each step, one by one, and you'll be able to spell any word you can think of!

1.   **Look** at the word.
2.   **Say** the letters out loud.
3.   **Cover** the word.
4.   **Write** it from memory.
5.   **Check** by uncovering the word.

Learn to spell these sight words using the **look**, **say**, **cover**, **write**, **check** method.

do   _ _

their   _ _ _ _ _

many   _ _ _ _

said   _ _ _ _

beautiful   _ _ _ _ _ _ _ _ _

when   _ _ _ _

come   _ _ _ _

they   _ _ _ _

because   _ _ _ _ _ _ _

people   _ _ _ _ _ _

house   _ _ _ _ _

would   _ _ _ _ _

went   _ _ _ _

...to understand syllables

Syllables are the number of parts in a word that you can hear when you say a word.

Example:

The word **today** has two syllables because you can hear two parts of the word when you say it.

today
to - day
(1)   (2)

Try saying the word slowly and clapping your hands for each bit.

If you play a musical instrument or like listening to music, the syllables are like the beats that you can hear.

Some words have more than two syllables.

Saturday
Sat - ur - day
(1)   (2)   (3)

candyfloss
can - dy - floss
(1)   (2)   (3)

Knowing about syllables can help you with spelling because you can break words up into smaller parts to spell.

These puzzles contain words split into syllables.

Join each jigsaw piece to another to make a word.
Then write the word.

SNOW

NET

MAG

IC

CAR

MAN

COM

PET

Here are some bits of words. Match the parts of the word to make a
new word and write it on the line. The first one has been done for you.

hand   sent   sis weim

sis   dy

pre   bag   handbag

ted   lo

hel   ter

Let's practise words with more than one syllable.

Can you spell these words by breaking them into syllables?
The first one has been done for you.

inside   looking   about

i n / s i d e   _ _ _ _ _ _ _   _ _ _ _ _

banker   terrible   telescope

_ _ _ _ _ _   _ _ _ _ _ _ _ _   _ _ _ _ _ _ _ _ _

holiday   policeman   sister

_ _ _ _ _ _ _   _ _ _ _ _ _ _ _ _   _ _ _ _ _ _

Now choose four of those words and learn them, using

LOOK, SAY, COVER, WRITE, CHECK.   1 _____

2 _____

3 _____

4 _____

Read each word, then cover it up quickly.
See if you can spell it and mark where each syllable ends.
Then check it and underline any bits you got wrong.

annoying   natural   Saturday

_____   _____ _____

asteroid   talented   acrobatic

_____   _____ _____

Choose three words to learn, using

LOOK, **SAY**, **COVER**, **WRITE**, **CHECK**.

When you SAY the letters, shout or sing the bit you got wrong!
This will help you remember.

1. _____
2. _____
3. _____

Spell these words that are in the picture.

1 shel

2 jet

3 flag

4 boi

5 sun

6 pebl

7 wat

Spell these words that are in the picture.

1

2

3

4

5

6

7

8

Answers

page 37

c<u>ar</u>, f<u>ar</u>, st<u>ar</u>t, d<u>ar</u>t
b<u>oat</u>, fl<u>oat</u>, c<u>oat</u>, <u>oat</u>, m<u>oat</u>
c<u>oat</u>, b<u>oat</u>
f<u>ight</u>, s<u>ight</u>, r<u>ight</u>, t<u>ight</u>, l<u>ight</u>
night

page 39

fry
frost
frog

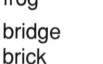

bridge
brick
brim

tree
trick
train

page 40

dress
draw
drip

grape
grow
grass

crab
cream
cry

page 41

clown
claw
cloud

planet
plum
plant

flag
flame
flower

page 43

duck, sock, kick,
sack, neck

The king ruled all the land.
Sarah got a ring for her birthday.
Ben is in the choir. He likes to sing
The phone rang so I answered it.

page 44

and
hand
bend
band
send
stand

74

Jimmy took a big gulp of
his orange juice.
Karen decided to help her mum
with the shopping.
The puppy let out a yelp when
the postman walked up the path.

page 45

best
fast
last
blast
chest
forest

Hannah put her pocket money in
the bank.
When Joe took his T-shirt out of
the washing-machine it had shrunk.
Harold began to think about his
summer holiday.

page 47

days, hands, cups, insects,
cookers, dolls, pandas

witches, kisses, foxes, boxes,

bushes, wishes, matches

page 48

bays, trays, toys, keys

ponies, nappies, puppies, fairies

parties, poppies, plays, days

page 49

sheep
teeth
women
children
men

page 51

Too many sweets
are bad for your
teeth.
The king and queen
spent a week at
their castle.
Your feet smell
really bad!

I let an old lady sit on my seat on
the bus.
I made sure my bedroom was
neat and tidy.
Mum took us to the fair for a treat.

sweet, queen, seat, meat

page 52

I can't speak. I have a sore throat.
Does ice sink or float?
The infants performed a show for the juniors.
I put my tooth under my pillow for the tooth fairy.
My dad hit the golf ball into the hole.
After going on holiday it is always nice to go back home.

boat, coat, pillow

page 53

I told a lie to my teacher. She was very cross.
For tea we ate steak and kidney pie.
The opposite of day is night.
The box was too high up for me to reach.
The birds decided to fly south for the winter.
Why did the chicken cross the road?

night, pie, tie

page 55

I. You will annoy me if you destroy my toy.
2. Don't boil the soup or you will spoil it.
3. I don't enjoy it when you point at me.

noise
boy
joy
joint
tomboy
tortoise

page 56

paint
train
play
snail
tray

faint
sway
clay
waist
stay

page 57

Accept any correctly spelt words with oi, oy, ay, and ai.

76

page 59

clapping
sipping
hopping
getting
swimming
cutting
shopping
running

page 60

looking
smiling
eating
waving
taking
coming
biting
sleeping

watched
jumped
laughed
climbed
clapped
shared
hopped
dared

page 61

Yesterday I walked up a big hill with my dad. We climbed up a very steep rock. I could see children swimming in the lake below. Some people were sitting at the side of the lake.

Last Saturday, I went shopping with my mum. On the way to the bus stop we walked past a hairdresser's. A lady was cutting a little girl's hair. We couldn't stop laughing because the girl was pulling a really grumpy face!

page 63

dolphin
alphabet
elephant
Christopher
trophy
pheasant
phone

page 64

photo, graph, phone
I took lots of photos on holiday.
My mum keeps telling me to
get off the phone!
My grandma doesn't eat turkey
on Christmas day, she eats
pheasant instead.
I can say the alphabet
backwards!

page 65

wheel, why, what, white, when,
where, which, whisper
words that ask questions:
why, what, when, where, which

who, what, where, when, why,
which
Which of these buns do you want?
What is the answer?
Where are you going to?
Who is hiding?
Why do balls bounce?
When is your birthday?

page 69

snowman
magnet
carpet
comic

sister
present
teddy
hello

page 70

in/side
look/ing
a/bout
ban/ker
ter/ri/ble
tel/e/scope
hol/i/day
pol/ice/man
sis/ter

Your child may break the syllables
at different points.

page 71

a/nnoy/ing
nat/u/ral
Sat/ur/day
as/ter/oid
ta/len/ted
a/cro/ba/tic

page 73

1. pipe
2. dog
3. moon
4. snowman
5. bird
6. tree
7. scarf
8. hat

page 72

1. shell
2. boat or ship
3. flag
4. boy
5. sun
6. sand
7. waves or sea

Very Well Done!

Words...

letter
sounds
word
consonant
consonant cluster
vowel
singular
plural
spelling pattern
syllable
pattern words
sight words

After working through each section, put a tick in the box to show how you feel about the topic.

If you tick 'Not sure' go back to those pages and try again.

	Confident	Not sure
Pattern words		
Sight words		
Beginning spellings		
End spellings		
Plurals		
Spelling different sounds		
Spelling **oi**, **oy**, **ai**, **ay**		
Adding **ing** and **ed**		
Words with **ph** and **wh**		
Syllables		
Spelling pictures		

Now you know!

Before you try the writing exercises in this book, think hard about the following things:

• If you want to write a long word but don't know how to spell it, 'sound out' the bits (syllables) of the word one at a time.

Example: adventurous   **ad-ven-chu-rus**

Then ask a parent to help you or look in the dictionary for the right spelling.

• Don't start all your sentences in the same way.

Example: I went to school in the morning. Then I had my lunch on the field. Then I had my afternoon lessons. Then I went home.

Think of different words to 'then' – next, after, etc, to make your writing more interesting.

• Make sure that **every** sentence starts with a **capital letter** and ends in a **full stop**.
A sentence is a collection of words that makes sense.
If it doesn't make sense it isn't a sentence.

Sentence	**Not a sentence**
The baby has no hair.	The baby hair.
My grandma is deaf.	My grandma is.
The water was deep.	Water was deep.

Start by writing a story about yourself. Include information about your friends and family and where you live. You could also write about your favourite pop group or hobby.

How...

...to understand character

The people or animals in a story are called the **characters**.
When you write a story, think very carefully about your characters:
• what they look like
• where they live
• what sort of person they are

This is the beginning of the fairy tale 'Cinderella'.
Read it and see how the writer has described the main character.

Cinderella

There was once a girl called Cinderella who wore old, torn, shabby clothes. She was a very shy girl and did what she was told. Cinderella's wicked stepmother made her do all the dirty work in the house. She washed the floors and dusted the bedrooms. Cinderella obediently helped to dress her two sisters for the ball at the palace. She wished them to have a good time.

Here are some notes about the character:

Name	What they look like	What sort of person
Cinderella	**wears old, torn, shabby clothes**	**very shy, obedient does what she is told**

Here's an example of how the story can change if we change the notes about the character.

Name	What they look like	What sort of person
Glimmerbell	**wears elegant, silky, expensive clothes**	**very confident disobedient mean spoilt**

Glimmerbell

There was once a girl called <u>Glimmerbell</u> who wore <u>elegant, silky, expensive</u> clothes. She was a very <u>confident</u> girl and <u>never</u> did what she was told. <u>Glimmerbell's</u> wicked stepmother made her do all the dirty work in the house. <u>But Glimmerbell refused to and had a tantrum every time she was asked. Glimmerbell made her sisters dress themselves</u> for the ball at the palace. <u>She told them she hoped no one would dance with them!</u>

The story has really changed!
So the way you describe your character is very important in your story.

Thinking about your characters carefully can really make your story very exciting and interesting.

Here are some different notes for the Cinderella character.
Choose a few of the descriptions to make up your own new character for the story.
Once you have chosen them, write them in the spaces below.

Name	What they look like	What sort of person
Jollyella Mousey Moodykins Raggabella	tall and slim scruffy tiny always smiling always frowning wears smart, clean clothes wears old, ragged clothes wears brightly coloured clothes	happy shy grumpy lazy quiet loud naughty

Name	What they look like	What sort of person
_____	_____ _____ _____ _____ _____	_____ _____ _____ _____ _____

Now fill in the story describing **your** new character. Make sure your story makes sense. If you describe your character as quiet then don't have them shouting at everyone! Look back at the story on page 84 to help you.

(The name of your character)

_____

There was once a girl called

_____ who wore

_____

clothes. She was a very _____

girl and _____ did what she

was told. _____'s

wicked stepmother made her do

all the dirty work in the house.

_____

_____

_____

_____

for the ball at the palace. _____

_____

_____

_____ .

Draw a picture of your character.

...to use settings

How...

The setting of a story is **where** a story takes place, for example:
- in a castle
- underground
- on the beach
- at the North Pole

The setting can also tell you **when** the story happens, for example:
- long ago in the past
- far into the future
- right now in the present

Read this story and look at the notes about the setting.

David and the Giant

Hundreds of years ago there was a boy called David. He looked after his father's sheep out on the hills in Israel. All day long he watched the sheep and played with his slingshot. One of the king's enemies was a huge man called Goliath. He was ten feet tall! No one was brave enough to fight him, except David.

Where

in the hills in Israel

When

hundreds of years ago in the past

What are the settings of these stories?
The first one has been done for you.

The spaceship landed on Mars and the aliens jumped out. They had been to Earth to get food. The aliens had become good friends with the humans on Earth.

Where? __Mars__
__space__
_____
When? __some time in the future__
_____
_____

Long, long ago in an ancient forest, some fairies were flying in and out of the flowers. They were casting spells to make the plants grow. Suddenly, they saw a little girl running towards them – they had to hide!

Where? _____
_____
_____
When? _____
_____
_____

It was six o'clock on an early Sunday morning. Jake was in the paper shop filling his bag. He had a lot of houses to deliver to that morning.

Where? _____
_____
_____
When? _____
_____
_____

Writers usually talk about the setting at the **beginning** of a story.
This way the reader can clearly imagine what is happening in the story.

Write a story about your favourite day out.
Before you start the story, make some notes about **when** and **where** the day took place.

When

Where

Use these notes to begin your story below.

My favourite day

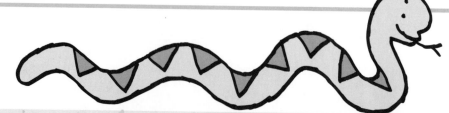

Now continue your story here.

Remember to include lots of details about the people (characters) in your story.

How...

...to structure stories

All stories need a good structure.

Structure means having a clear **beginning**, **middle** and **ending**.

If any part of a story was missing the reader wouldn't understand what was going on!

Example:

The Ugly Duckling

Beginning

A mother duck sat on her nest waiting for her eggs to hatch. She had been waiting a long, long time. Tap, tap tap! All the ducklings popped out of the eggs. But the last duckling was ever so ugly and clumsy-looking.

Middle

All the other animals teased the ugly duckling because he looked different. Feeling very sad, the ugly duckling left the farm. It was winter and he grew cold and hungry.

Ending

But soon spring came and the ugly duckling spread his wings and flew over the lake. When he landed on the water the ugly duckling looked at his reflection. He was no longer an ugly duckling but a beautiful swan!

Here is a well-known story. It has been split into a beginning, middle and ending – but someone has jumbled them up!

Try and work out the correct order, then write the letters below.

A   Goldilocks saw the open door to the bears' cottage and went in. She tasted their porridge, sat in their chairs and fell asleep in Baby Bear's bed.

B   In a cottage in a wood lived three bears – Father Bear, Mother Bear and Baby Bear. Their porridge was too hot so they went for a walk whilst it cooled down.

C   When the bears returned they could tell someone had been in their cottage. Upstairs, they found Goldilocks asleep in Baby Bear's bed! But the bears weren't angry and invited Goldilocks for breakfast.

Order of story

Beginning   _____

Middle   _____

Ending   _____

The beginning, middle and ending of a story should follow a pattern.

Beginning   Tells you about the setting and the characters.

Middle   Tells you what happens to the characters. A problem
              usually develops.

Ending   Tells you what happens in the end. The problem is solved!

Think of a story you know very well.

Can you split the story into these parts?

Title _____

Beginning   _____

              _____

              _____

Middle   _____

              _____

              _____

Ending   _____

              _____

              _____

Now it's time for you to be a writer.

Write a story about a day at school when something unusual happened.

Plan your story here with notes about the beginning, middle and ending. Also write some notes about the characters who will appear.

Title _____

Beginning

_____

_____

_____

_____

Middle

_____

_____

_____

Ending

_____

_____

_____

Now you have planned your story, use the notes to write it out here.

Enjoy yourself – you're the writer after all!

When you have finished your story, show it to your family or even somebody who starred in the story!

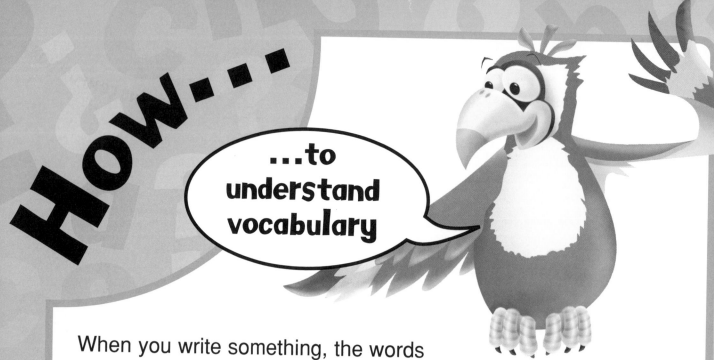

How...

...to understand vocabulary

When you write something, the words you choose are very important.
If you use dull words your story will be dull. But if you use exciting words your story will be more interesting.

A **synonym** is a word that has the same or nearly the same meaning as another word.

> **big** is a synonym of **large**
> **small** is a synonym of **little**

Here are some more synonyms.

like	love
angry	cross
happy	glad
start	begin
dull	boring

Rewrite this story at the bottom of the page.
For each underlined word think of another word that means the same thing.
Use the words in the box to help you.

One <u>wet</u> morning, Jacob pulled on his <u>wellies</u> and went out to play. At the back of Jacob's house there was a <u>huge</u> garden.

Jacob <u>ran</u> down to the bottom of the garden. He <u>stared</u> at the sky and could tell it was going to rain. So Jacob stood under the <u>ancient</u> oak tree.

Suddenly, it began to rain.

enormous	looked	old
rainy	rushed	boots

How...

...to use descriptive writing

When a writer writes a story or poem they have to describe exactly what they are imagining in their head.

Example:

I have a dog. → Can you tell what the dog looks like?

I have a big brown dog with floppy ears. → Can you tell if the dog is well behaved?

I have a big brown dog with floppy ears who is always getting into trouble! → This is much better!

When you are describing something (a person, place, animal) you should try and think about the following things:

size

shape   **colour**   **movement**

age

smell   **dislikes**   **likes**

Create a strange animal, insect or monster
and describe it in as much detail as you can.
If you describe it really well, the reader should
be able to picture exactly what it is like.

There are special words we can use to describe the **time** in which a story or poem happens.

Here are some simple ones: yesterday
tomorrow

There are some words that can describe a **sequence of events**. This means the order in which things happen.

Example:

> **When I had finished** washing the car, I decided to go for a walk. I walked along the path in the woods and **suddenly** something fell on my head! It was only a twig. **After** my walk I headed back home. **Before** I had put the key in the front door I felt a tap on my shoulder. It was my dad.

Here are some more words and phrases that describe time:

the next minute
an hour later
at that moment
when I had finished
suddenly
after that
before I had started to

Choose to write about one of the following items.
Describe the order in which things happened using
the words and phrases on page 102.

| A trip to the seaside | Making a cake | Building a tree-house | Going on a plane | Christmas Day |

Now is the time to put everything together.
Use the space below to make notes.
You can choose to write a funny or scary story.

Plan the structure and what the characters are like.
Use lots of interesting language and vary the time words you use.

Now write your story here.

How...

...to understand rhyme

Rhyming words have the same sound at the end.

book	–	cook	Say each pair of words out loud
pink	–	sink	and listen to how they sound.
slug	–	mug	Can you hear how they rhyme?

Read this poem out loud.

Georgie Porgie

Georgie Porgie, pudding and **pie**,
kissed the girls and made them **cry**.
When the boys came out to **play**,
Georgie Porgie ran **away**.

Look at where the rhyming words are.
In a poem the rhyming words come at the **end** of the sentences.
These are the rhyming words:

pie	–	cry
play	–	away

Let's see what happens when we take out the rhyming words and put some new ones in.

> Georgie Porgie, pudding and **cake**,
> kissed the girls and made them **shake**.
> When the boys came out to **run**,
> Georgie Porgie was no **fun**.

The rhyming words are:

cake   —   shake
run   —   fun

Now it's your turn.
Choose some rhyming words and fit them into the poem.

Humpty, Dumpty sat on the _____.
Humpty, Dumpty had a great _____.

> hay   bath   hill
>
>   day   laugh   thrill

Circle the rhyming words.

Hey diddle, diddle,
The cat and the fiddle.
The cow jumped over the moon.

I know a funny dog,
That thinks that it's a frog.
It loves to jump and jiggle.
This really makes me giggle!

Here is a rhyme you might not have heard before.

Oh, dear me!
My mother caught a flea.
She put it in the teapot,
and made a cup of tea.

Choose from these words to make a new, silly rhyme.

Oh, dear me!
My mother caught a _____ .
She put it in the teapot,
and made a cup of _____ .

coffee   bunny   honey

   toffee   moose   juice

Here is another rhyme.

Cobbler, cobbler, mend my shoe,
Get it done by half past two.

Choose from these words to make a new rhyme.

Cobbler, cobbler, mend my _____ ,
Get it done by half past _____ .

three   four   eight

   settee   door   plate

Now it's your turn to be a poet!

Think of some good rhyming words to use before you start to write your poem.

You can use the pictures for inspiration or write a poem about a friend or someone in your family.

How...

...to understand alliteration

Alliteration is a special word used to talk about words with the **same sound** that are close together in a sentence.
Example:

The **sc**ared **sk**unk **sc**urried away.

The letters **sc** and **sk** make the same sounds in this sentence. The letters are different but the sounds are the same and alliteration is all about the sounds in a sentence.

Here are some more sentences with alliteration.

The **sl**ow **sl**ug **sl**ithered and **sl**ipped.

The **gr**een giant **gr**owled and **gr**inned.

The **cr**azy **cr**ab **cr**ossed the road with an ice-**cr**eam!

The **fr**iendly **fr**og saved the **fr**eezing toad!

Choose two or three words from the box that start with the same sound.
Put them together to make a sentence.
Your sentence can be silly or sensible!

shampoo   twisted   black   shut   shower

two   bear   odd   omelette

orange   shuffled   bald   twinkled

twins   oil   octopus   sheep

blue   shark   belly

The two twins twisted their bodies.

How...

...to write tongue-twisters

Tongue-twisters are short rhymes or phrases that have similar sounds in them.

They have a bit of **alliteration** in them but also similar sounds that make the words tricky to say.

Read this tongue-twister out loud and listen to the sounds the words make.

> **She sells seashells on the seashore,**
> **The seashells she sells are seashells I'm sure!**

Did you get the tongue-twister tied up in knots?

The sounds **s** and **sh** are repeated in the tongue-twister.

Because these sounds are very similar they are difficult to say next to each other.

Here is another tongue-twister.

> **Betty better butter Brad's bread.**

The sounds **bett**, **butt** and **br** are similar in this tongue-twister.

How fast can you say it?

Let's see if you can write your own tongue-twister.

First decide who it will be about –
a famous person, yourself, or someone in your family.

Next, think of another sound that is similar to the first sound in the person's name.

Example:

The tongue-twister will be about Claire.
A sound similar to **cl** is **c**.

Clever Claire can clean cauliflowers!

Your tongue-twister will be about _____.

The sounds you will use are _____ and _____.

_____

_____

_____

_____

_____

113

How...

...to write letters

Letters should be written in a certain way.

The address goes at the top right corner → 51 Hill Avenue
Finshy
Devon
D53 7DH

Start your letter with 'Dear'.

The date goes under the address. → 13/8/02

Dear Penelope,

I'm writing to invite you to a surprise birthday party for our friend Sindy.

It will be on Saturday 14th July at my house.
Please could you arrive at 2pm because Sindy will be coming at about 2:30pm.

Make sure you don't tell Sindy because that will spoil the surprise!

Hope to see you there,
love Saskia.

xxx

If you are writing a letter to a friend your language can be quite chatty. **See you soon!** **Take care,** **Bye for now**!

If you are writing a letter to a stranger your language should be polite. **Yours faithfully** **Dear Sir/Madam** **Dear Mr/Mrs**

Now it's your turn to write a letter.
Write a thank-you letter for a present,
or a letter to a child from another country,
telling him or her about yourself.

How...

...to follow instructions

When you write instructions, you need to include **all** the information someone needs to know.

Example:

Instructions on how to make a cake.
If the writer misses out some ingredients or puts things in the wrong order, the reader will not be able to make the cake properly.

When you write instructions:
- put each instruction in the right order
- number each instruction in a list
- make sure each instruction follows on from the instruction before it

Here are instructions of how to get to Alice's school from her house:

1. Walk down the front path.

2. Turn left and walk to the end of the road.

3. Wait at the bus stop.

4. Get on the 370 bus.

5. Get off at the bus stop in front of the park.

6. Turn right and walk to the end of the road.

7. The school is on the left.

Write some very clear instructions on **one** of the following:

- how to get from your bedroom to the kitchen
- how to plant some seeds
- how to paint a picture

If you don't write clearly, the person reading the instructions might get lost or go wrong.

How...

...to use labels

Writing labels is a kind of non-fiction writing. You can write labels for lots of things:

things in your classroom   **doors**

pictures and diagrams   **maps**

Labels need to be very clear and help the reader understand what they are looking at. Only label things that **need** labelling – don't label **everything** in your classroom, including the floor – that would be silly!

This flower has been labelled.

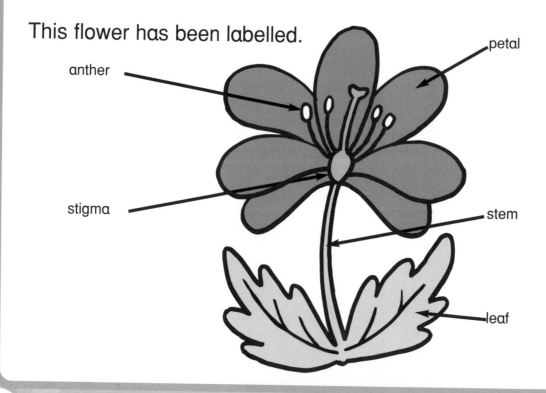

How good at labelling are you?
Here is a picture of a human body.
Choose from the labels at the bottom and write
them in the correct places.

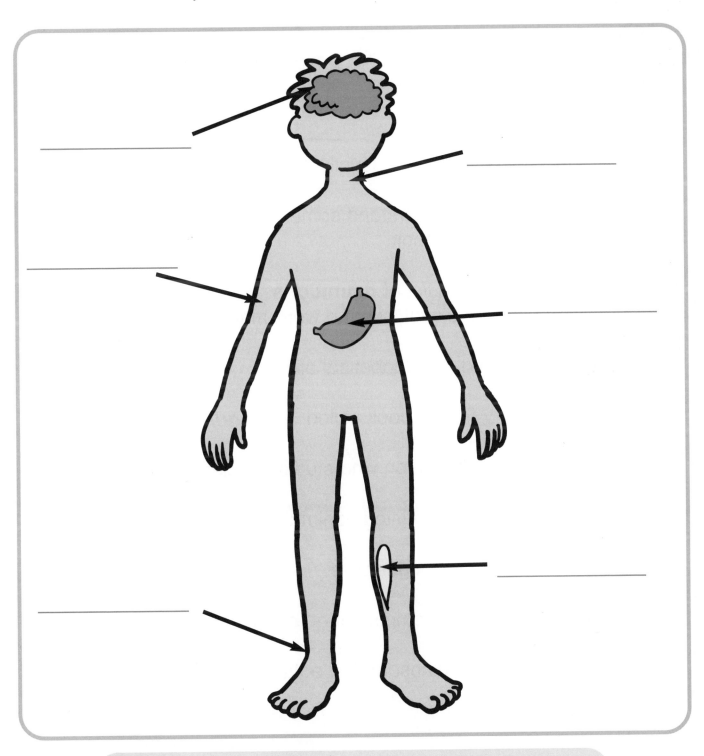

brain   calf   ankle
       arm   stomach   neck

A glossary is a list of words, usually at the back of a book.

It helps the reader to understand some of the words that have been mentioned in the book.

In a glossary there is a list of **definitions**.
A definition explains exactly what a word means.

Glossaries are listed in alphabetical order.

Here is a glossary from a book called *Dinosaurs*.

archaeologist   a person who studies ancient remains.

dinosaur   a prehistoric animal.

extinct   no longer alive.

fossils   the remains of an animal or plant.

stegosaurus   a dinosaur that eats plants.

Write your own glossary for one of the following books:
Computer games
Cars
Animals
Dogs

Think of which words would be useful to have in the glossary.
Which words might the reader not understand?
For each word write a definition.
Look up the words in a dictionary to help you.

_____   _____

                         _____

_____   _____

                         _____

_____   _____

                         _____

_____   _____

                         _____

_____   _____

                         _____

How...

...to use fact sheets

A fact sheet is usually one piece of paper giving you lots and lots of information about a topic.

It can have:

- diagrams or pictures
- puzzles and games
- instructions
- handy hints
- labels
- recipes
- lists
- jokes

Here is a fact sheet about exploring the outdoors.

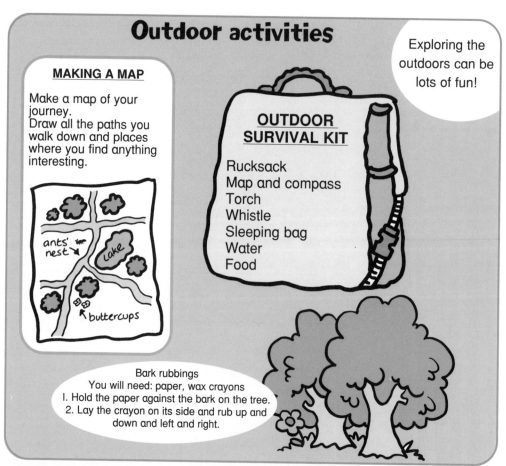

Outdoor activities

Exploring the outdoors can be lots of fun!

MAKING A MAP

Make a map of your journey.
Draw all the paths you walk down and places where you find anything interesting.

ants' nest
lake
buttercups

OUTDOOR SURVIVAL KIT

Rucksack
Map and compass
Torch
Whistle
Sleeping bag
Water
Food

Bark rubbings
You will need: paper, wax crayons
1. Hold the paper against the bark on the tree.
2. Lay the crayon on its side and rub up and down and left and right.

Now it's your turn to write your own fact sheet.
It can be about any topic you like.
Write as much information as you can.
Here are some ideas: football, hobbies, cooking,
TV programmes, film stars, pop singers.

Answers

page 87

Accept any story that shows a coherent understanding of character.

page 89

Where	–	in an ancient forest in the flowers
When	–	long, long ago in the past

Where	–	paper shop
When	–	6 o'clock in the morning Sunday

page 91

Accept any story that shows a coherent understanding and use of setting.

page 93

B, A, C

page 94

Check that your child has understood how to break a story into beginning, middle and ending.

page 99

wet	–	rainy
wellies	–	boots
huge	–	enormous
ran	–	rushed
stared	–	looked
ancient	–	old

or any other words that show an understanding

page 101

Accept any story that shows a good use of description.

page 103

Accept any story that shows a varied use of time words.

page 107

Accept any rhyming combination.
diddle	–	fiddle
dog	–	frog
jiggle	–	giggle

page 108

Accept any rhyming combination.

page 109

Accept any poem that shows a good understanding of rhyme.

page 111

Check that your child has used alliterative words.

page 115

Check that your child has followed the correct letter layout.

page 117

Accept any instructions that make sense.

page 119

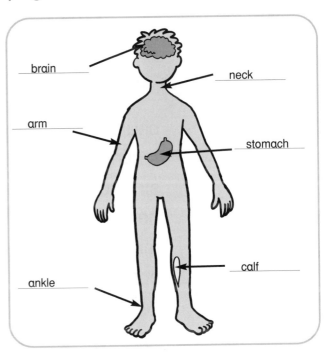

brain
neck
arm
stomach
ankle
calf

page 121

Accept any clear definitions.

Great work!

Words...

...you have learnt

character
setting
structure
beginning
middle
ending
vocubulary
synonym
description
sequence
rhyme
inspiration
alliteration
tongue-twister

letter
instructions
labels
glossary
definition
alphabetical
information
fact sheet

After working through each section, put a tick in the box to show how you feel about the topic.

If you tick 'Not sure' go back to those pages and try again.

	Confident	Not sure
Character	⬭	⬭
Setting	⬭	⬭
Structure	⬭	⬭
Vocabulary	⬭	⬭
Description	⬭	⬭
Language of time	⬭	⬭
Rhyme	⬭	⬭
Alliteration	⬭	⬭
Tongue-twisters	⬭	⬭
Letters	⬭	⬭
Instructions	⬭	⬭
Labels	⬭	⬭
Glossary	⬭	⬭
Fact sheets	⬭	⬭

Now you know!

> Look out for other **MEGA** titles for both 5-7 AND 7-9 year olds!

Other MEGA titles:

Mega Maths 5-7   ISBN: 0 7498 5771 4
Mega Maths 7-9   ISBN: 0 7498 5466 9
Mega English 7-9   ISBN: 0 7498 5467 7

Each book is packed with 128 pages of maths or English practice with 100 fun stickers to enjoy.

All titles comply with the National Curriculum (England and Wales) and English and Mathematics 5-14 (Scotland) and are in line with the National Literacy and Numeracy Strategies.

These are the perfect books to guide your child's development through school.